Heaven in a Poem

To Emma, Keli, James & Jack

Compiled by Lois Rock
Designed by Nicky Farthing
Illustrations copyright © 2000 Christopher Corr
This edition copyright © 2000 Lion Publishing

The moral rights of the compiler and illustrator
have been asserted

Published by
Lion Publishing plc
Sandy Lane West, Oxford, England
www.lion-publishing.co.uk
ISBN 0 7459 4259 8

First edition 2000
10 9 8 7 6 5 4 3 2 1 0

A catalogue record for this book is available
from the British Library

Typeset in 14/20 Baskerville MT
Printed and bound in Singapore

Acknowledgments
Thanks go to all those who have given permission to include material in
this book, as indicated in the list below. Every effort has been made to trace
and contact copyright owners. We apologize for any inadvertent omissions
or errors.

'Fiddler's Green' by J.A. Connolly, used by permission of March Music.
'Imaginary Daylight', copyright © Kate Farrell. First published in *Art & Wonder:
An Illustrated Anthology of Visionary Poetry*, The Metropolitan Museum of Art
and Bulfinch Press, 1996. Reprinted by permission of the author and The
Metropolitan Museum of Art. 'My Kite', 'My Rabbit' and 'I Like it Here' by
Christina Goodings, copyright © 2000 Lion Publishing. 'The Land That Breaks
Beyond Our Dreams' from the collection *Limited Edition* by Stewart Henderson,
published by Plover Books. Copyright © 1997 Stewart Henderson. 'Very Quiet',
copyright © 2000 Jack Jiggens. 'Candy Floss Heaven', copyright © 2000
Keli Jiggens. 'The Shore Beyond' and 'A Boat Made for One' by Mary Joslin,
copyright © 2000 Lion Publishing. 'I Think Heaven Will Have', copyright
© 2000 Emma Kew. 'When Earth's Last Picture is Painted' by Rudyard
Kipling, from the writings of Rudyard Kipling, used by permission of A.P.
Watt Ltd on behalf of The National Trust for Places of Historic Interest
or Natural Beauty. 'Heaven's Walls', copyright © 2000 James Parkinson.
'Exile', copyright © Evangeline Paterson. 'Nocturn' by Kathleen Raine, used
by permission of Lindisfarne Books, Hudson, NY 12534. 'Music Practice' and
'God's Computer' by Mark Robinson, copyright © 2000 Lion Publishing.
'The Road Goes Ever On', from *The Lord of the Rings* by J.R.R. Tolkien, used
by permission of HarperCollins Publishers Ltd. 'Heaven', copyright © 1999
Steve Turner. 'Holy Snails', copyright © John Wells. Reproduced by permission
of the author's estate c/o Rogers, Coleridge & White Ltd., 20 Powis Mews,
London W11 1JN. 'Boring', copyright © John Whitworth.

Heaven
in a
Poem

An anthology of poems

Compiled by Lois Rock
Illustrated by Christopher Corr

LION
Children's Books

The Road

The Road goes ever on and on
    Down from the door where it began.
Now far ahead the Road has gone,
    And I must follow, if I can,
Pursuing it with eager feet,
    Until it joins some larger way
Where many paths and errands meet.
    And whither then? I cannot say.

J.R.R. Tolkien (1892–1973)

Hope

Hope is the thing with feathers
That perches in the soul,
And sings the tune without the words
And never stops at all,

And sweetest in the gale is heard;
And sore must be the storm
That could abash the little bird
That kept so many warm.

I've heard it in the chillest land,
And on the strangest sea;
Yet, never, in extremity,
It asked a crumb of me.

Emily Dickinson (1830–86)

Past: Present: Future

'Tell me, tell me, smiling child,
What the Past is like to thee.'
'An Autumn evening soft and mild
With a wind that sighs mournfully.'

'Tell me what is the Present hour.'
'A green and flowery spray,
Where a young bird sits gathering its power
To mount and fly away.'

'And what is the Future, happy one?'
'A sea beneath a cloudless sun:
A mighty glorious dazzling sea
Stretching into Infinity.'

Emily Brontë (1818–48)

Holy Snails

In Paradise the Blessed Snails
They say lay solid silver trails
Advancing with their slow caress
Along the Paths of Righteousness

They have great shells of beaten gold
Bejewelled skirts that spread and fold
Twin pearly horns that search and blink
On stretching necks of diamond link

Gliding beside the Glassy Sea
They weave their shining tracery
Up uncut crags of precious stone
To summits known to God alone

There, high against the emerald sky
They lift their happy horns and sigh
Contented, having laid with Grace
Their winding trail of silver lace

So if you see a snail today
Remember, though its shell is grey
A snail of most especial worth
May lay a silver trail on earth

John Wells (Modern poet)

Birds of Paradise

Golden-winged, silver-winged,
  Winged with flashing flame,
Such a flight of birds I saw,
  Birds without a name:
Singing songs in their own tongue—
  Song of songs—they came.

They flashed and they darted
  Awhile before mine eyes,
Mounting, mounting, mounting still,
  In haste to scale the skies,
Birds without a nest on earth,
  Birds of Paradise.

Christina Rossetti (1830–94)

My Kite

Up on the hill on a windy day
I let my kite blow far away—
Higher and higher in the sky
Where great white clouds go sailing by.
An angel with a golden wing
Must have caught it by the string,
But getting the tangles out for me
Is taking an eternity.

Christina Goodings (Modern poet)

My Rabbit

When I get to Heaven (and I'll make sure that I do)
I want to check that it's well run:
I'm worried that the angels won't take good care
    of my rabbit—
Can they tell when a rabbit's having fun?

Do they bring him lettuce when he'd rather nibble
    carrots?
Do they fill his hutch with hay or bits of cloud?
Does he have to speak politely to guinea pigs?—
    (he hates them),
He's a prizewinning rabbit and he's proud.

It's sort of nice to dream that my rabbit is in Heaven
And in Heaven's starry meadows running free.
But I really wish he'd burrow down through
    Heaven's bright blue floor
And come skipping, hopping, jumping back to me.

Christina Goodings (Modern poet)

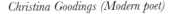

Music Practice

You can't go to heaven,
No you can't go to heaven
With your music lessons only just begun.
You can't even play recorder
And you're only on the borderline
Of keeping to a rhythm on a drum.

You'll have to learn the cymbal
And the trumpet and the harp
And the lyre and the zither as well.
For if you get notes wrong
Then the angels stop their song
And they send you away to
Practise.

Mark Robinson (Modern poet)

God's Computer

They say there's a heaven where all people go.
What I've heard makes me feel quite uneasy.
For all that you've done is there read out aloud
The thought of it makes me go queasy.

The things that I've done and the things that I've said
Have not always been funny or clever;
And yet in a book where the angels can look
People say they are noted for ever.

I just hope that God will move on with the times
With computers for all of his data.
I'll hack my way in and delete every sin
And turn up at the gates a bit later.

Mark Robinson (Modern poet)

Boring

I'm dead bored,
    bored to the bone.
Nobody likes me,
    I'm all alone.
I'll just go crawl
    under a stone.

Hate my family,
    got no friends,
I'll sit here till
    the universe ends
Or I starve to death—
    it all depends.

Then I'll be dead,
    dead and rotten,
Less than a blot when
    it's been well blotten,
Less than a teddy bear
    that's been forgotten.

Then I'll go to Heaven which
    is more than can be said
For certain persons
    when they're dead.
They'll go you-know-
    where instead.

Then they'll be sorry,
    Then they'll be glum,
Sitting on a stove till
    Kingdom Come.
Then they can all go
    kiss my…
Hmm, that's a sort of swearing;
    people shouldn't swear.
I won't go to Heaven but
    I don't care,
    I don't care,
    I don't care.
I'll sit here and swear
    so there.

Except that it's boring…

John Whitworth (Modern poet)

I Like it Here

I'm not going off to Heaven
Unless you're coming too;
I like it here on Earth
Where there's such a lot to do.
And if I met an angel
I don't know what I'd say.
Unless you're coming with me
It's here I'm going to stay.

Christina Goodings (Modern poet)

Heaven

What happens in heaven?
Will I sit on a cloud?
Is walking or talking
Or jumping allowed?

Will I be on my own
Or with some of my friends?
Does it go on for ever
Or eventually end?

What happens in heaven?
Will I play a harp's strings?
I can't play piano
I can't even sing.

Who chooses the music
That angels inspire?
Who does the auditions
For the heavenly choir?

What happens in heaven?
Are the streets paved with gold?
Is it crowded with people
Who're incredibly old?

Will I know who I am?
Will I know what I'm called?
If I pinch myself hard
Will I feel it at all?

What happens in heaven?
Do I go through a gate?
What if I get myself lost
Or turn up too late?

Is my name on a list?
Is the gatekeeper nice?
Can you sneak in for nothing
Or is there a price?

Steve Turner (Modern poet)

Message of Love

Here's a message of love,
Come down from above,
To invite little children to heaven:
In God's blessed book
Poor sinners may look,
And see how all sins are forgiven.

Children's hymn

A Carol for Children

The Shepherds had an Angel,
The Wise Men had a star,
But what have I, a little child,
To guide me home from far,
Where glad stars sing together
And singing angels are?—

Lord Jesus is my guiding star,
My beacon-light in heaven:
He leads me step by step along
The path of life uneven:
He, true light, leads me to that land
Whose day shall be as seven.

Those Shepherds through the lonely night
Sat watching by their sheep,
Until they saw the heavenly host
Who neither tire nor sleep,
All singing 'Glory glory'
In festival they keep.

Christ watches me, His little lamb,
Cares for me day and night,
That I may be His own in heaven:
So angels clad in white
Shall sing their 'Glory glory'
For my sake in the height.

The Wise Men left their country
To journey morn by morn,
With gold and frankincense and myrrh,
Because the Lord was born:
God sent a star to guide them
And sent a dream to warn.

My life is like their journey,
Their star is like God's book;
I must be like those good Wise Men
With heavenward heart and look:
But shall I give no gifts to God?—
What precious gifts they took!

Lord, I will give my love to Thee,
Than gold much costlier,
Sweeter to Thee than frankincense,
More prized than choicest myrrh:
Lord, make me dearer day by day,
Day by day holier;

Nearer and dearer day by day:
Till I my voice unite,
And sing my 'Glory glory'
With angels clad in white;
All 'Glory glory' given to Thee
Through all the heavenly height.

Christina Rossetti (1830–94)

Imaginary Daylight

At night above my bed
The shadows of the shutters
Float on the ceiling
And, through the slats, leaves shiver
In the breeze from the river
As the streetlamp glow
Dissolves all the floors
Of the building above me,
Illumining a country
Of gardens, arbors, fountains
Where people talk about momentous things
With perfect kindness and quiet certainty,
And I am the grubworm who sleeps in the soil
Beneath the beautiful paths
Where they are thinking and walking.

Kate Farrell (Modern poet)

Nocturn

Night comes, an angel stands
Measuring out the time of stars,
Still are the winds, and still the hours.

It would be peace to lie
Still in the still hours at the angel's feet,
Upon a star hung in a starry sky,
But hearts another measure beat.

Each body, wingless as it lies,
Sends out its butterfly of night
With delicate wings and jewelled eyes.

And some upon day's shores are cast,
And some in darkness lost
In waves beyond the world, where float
Somewhere the islands of the blest.

Kathleen Raine (Modern poet)

Golden String

I give you the end of a golden string,
Only wind it into a ball:
It will lead you in at Heaven's gate,
Built in Jerusalem's wall.

William Blake (1757–1827)

Uphill

Does the road wind uphill all the way?
Yes, to the very end.
Will the day's journey take the whole long day?
From morn to night, my friend.

But is there for the night a resting-place?
A roof for when the slow, dark hours begin.
May not the darkness hide it from my face?
You cannot miss that inn.

Shall I meet other wayfarers at night?
Those who have gone before.
Then must I knock, or call when just in sight?
They will not keep you standing at that door.

Shall I find comfort, travel-sore and weak?
Of labour you shall find the sum.
Will there be beds for me and all who seek?
Yea, beds for all who come.

Christina Rossetti (1830–94)

The Shore Beyond

A lonely shoreline, dark and cold;

Beyond—perhaps—a land of gold;

A land where sorrow melts away,

Where friends are found, where loved ones play.

A land of laughter and delight…

Perhaps, beyond; but here, it's night.

Yet, now and then, the shadows part,

When love and kindess touch the heart.

Then gold light streams from some far shore:

The light of love for evermore.

Mary Joslin (Modern poet)

The Boat Made for One

One weary evening, alone I went down,
Down to the grey-green sea;
And there on the shore was a boat made for one,
A boat that was waiting for me.

I picked up the paddle and floated away
On a path of gold lit by the sun
Over the shifting grey-green swell
In a tiny boat made just for one.

Far out to sea the waves grew more wild—
Towering, menacing, grey;
Myself and the little boat made just for one
Had become the great ocean's prey.

On a mountaintop crest I went up to the sky
Then down in a vale of the sea
And then I was flung upside down on the deep,
The boat made for one and me.

But just when I thought I was lost in the dark
A wave turned me back all aright.
In a glittering world of diamond spray
My boat took me safe to the light.

Mary Joslin (Modern poet)

Crossing over

May the Father take you
In His fragrant clasp of love,
When you go across the flooding
    streams
And the black river of death.

From Carmina Gadelica

The Key of the Kingdom

This is the Key of the Kingdom:
In that Kingdom is a city;
In that city is a town;
In that town there is a street;
In that street there winds a lane;
In that lane there is a yard;
In that yard there is a house;
In that house there waits a room
In that room an empty bed
And on that bed a basket—
A Basket of Sweet Flowers;
Of Flowers, of Flowers;
A Basket of Sweet Flowers.

Flowers in a Basket;
Basket on the bed;
Bed in the chamber;
Chamber in the house;
House in the weedy yard;
Yard in the winding lane;
Lane in the broad street;
Street in the high town;
Town in the city;
City in the Kingdom—
This is the Key of the Kingdom;
Of the Kingdom this is the Key.

Anonymous

Candyfloss Heaven

Heaven is a place full of pink clouds
nice and bright
lots of flowers
where no one can see you
and it never becomes night
and it never becomes morning
because there's no time
just lots of candyfloss.
There is singing all around.

Keli Jiggens (aged 9)

A Better World

There is a better world above,
   Oh, so bright!
Where all is peace, and joy, and love,
   Oh, so bright!
And all are free from every care,
And Jesus Christ the Lord is there,
And harps of God, and mansions fair,
   Oh, so bright!

Children's hymn

Very Quiet

It's a place where God is sitting on the cloud
Guarding the gate with his thunder bolts
It's a place with a big palace
And there are lots of fairies and angels
With no shops and no cars and no beaches
And it's very quiet.

Jack Jiggens (aged 7)

Heaven's Walls

Heaven's walls are golden, bright,
And the walls are shuddering with the voice
  of the angels.
There are lanterns hanging from the walls
And you see dead friends or family waving
  to you.
As you step through the gates, angels cheer.
You are through Heaven's walls.

James Parkinson (aged 8)

A Happy Land

There is a happy land,
  Far, far away;
Where saints in glory stand,
  Bright, bright as day.
Oh, how they sweetly sing!
Worthy is the Saviour King;
Loud let His praises ring,
  Praise, praise for aye.

Andrew Young (1807–89)

Fiddler's Green

As I roved by the dock side one evening so rare
To view the still waters and take the salt air,
I heard an old fisherman singing this song:
'Take me away boys, me time is not long.'

Dress me up in me oil skins and jumper,
No more on the docks I'll be seen;
Just tell me old ship mates I'm taking a trip mates
And I'll see you someday in Fiddler's Green.

Now Fiddler's Green is a place I've heard tell,
Where Fishermen go if they don't go to hell.
The weather is fair and the dolphins do play,
And the cold coast of Greenland is far, far away.

The sky's always clear and there's never a gale,
And the fish jump on board with a flip of their tail.
You can lie at your leisure, there's no work to do,
And the skipper's below making tea for the crew.

I don't want a harp or a halo, not me,
Just give me a breeze and a good rolling sea,
And I'll play me old squeeze box as we sail along,
With the wind in the rigging to sing me this song:

J.A. Connolly (Modern poet)

When Earth's Last Picture is Painted

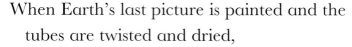

When Earth's last picture is painted and the
    tubes are twisted and dried,
When the oldest colours have faded, and the
    youngest critic has died,
We shall rest, and, faith, we shall need it—lie
    down for an aeon or two,
Till the Master of All Good Workmen shall
    put us to work anew.

And those that were good shall be happy: they
    shall sit in a golden chair;
They shall splash at a ten-league canvas with
    brushes of comets' hair.
They shall find real saints to draw from—
    Magdalene, Peter, and Paul;
They shall work for an age at a sitting and
    never be tired at all!

And only The Master shall praise us, and only
    The Master shall blame;
And no one shall work for money, and no one
    shall work for fame,
But each for the joy of the working, and each,
    in his separate star,
Shall draw the Thing as he sees it for the
    God of Things as they are!

Rudyard Kipling (1865–1936)

Looking Upward Every Day

Looking upward every day,
   Sunshine on our faces;
Pressing onward every day
   Toward the heavenly places.

Leaving every day behind
   Something which might hinder;
Running swifter every day,
   Growing purer, kinder.

Lord, so pray we every day,
   Hear us in Thy pity,
That we enter in at last
   To the Holy City.

Mary Butler (1841–1916)

Echo

O who will show me those delights on high?
    Echo.   I.
Thou Echo, thou art mortal, all men know.
    Echo.   No.
Wert thou not born among the trees and leaves?
    Echo.   Leaves.
And are there any leaves, that still abide?
    Echo.   Bide.
What leaves are they? impart the matter wholly.
    Echo.   Holy.

Are holy leaves the Echo then of bliss?
    Echo.   Yes.
Then tell me, what is that supreme delight?
    Echo.   Light.
Light to the mind; what shall the will enjoy?
    Echo.   Joy.
But are there cares and business with the pleasure?
    Echo.   Leisure.
Light, joy, and leisure; but shall they persevere?
    Echo.   Ever.

George Herbert (1593–1633)

Exile

Yes, it is beautiful country,
the streams in the winding valley,
the knowes and the birches,
and beautiful the mountain's bare shoulder
and the calm brows of the hills,
but it is not my country,
and in my heart there is a hollow place always.

And there is no way to go back—
maybe the miles indeed, but the years never.

Winding are the roads that we choose,
and inexorable is life,
driving us, it seems, like cattle
farther and farther away from what we remember.

But when we shall come at last
to God, who is our home and country,
there will be no more road stretching before us
and no more need to go back.

Evangeline Paterson (Modern poet)

The Journey

Whither, pilgrims, are you going,
  Going each with staff in hand?
We are going on a journey,
  Going at our King's command.
Over hills, and plains, and valleys,
We are going to His palace,
We are going to His palace,
  Going to the better land.

Tell us, pilgrims, what you hope for
  In that far-off better land.
Spotless robes, and crowns of glory,
  From a Saviour's loving hand.
We shall drink of life's clear river,
We shall dwell with God for ever,
We shall dwell with God for ever,
  In that bright, that better land.

Pilgrims, may we travel with you,
  To that bright and better land?
Come and welcome, come and welcome,
  Welcome to our pilgrim band
Come, oh come, and do not leave us;
Christ is waiting to receive us,
Christ is waiting to receive us,
  In that bright, that better land.

Children's hymn

The Golden City

Have you heard the golden city
  Mentioned in the legends old?
Everlasting light shines o'er it,
  Wondrous tales of it are told;
Only righteous men and women
  Dwell within its gleaming wall,
Wrong is banished from its borders,
  Justice reigns supreme o'er all.

Dr Felix Adler (1851–1933)

A Friend for Little Children

There's a Friend for little children,
  Above the bright blue sky,
A Friend who never changeth,
  Whose love can never die.
Unlike our friends by nature,
  Who change with changing years,
This Friend is always worthy
  The precious name He bears.

There's a home for little children,
  Above the bright blue sky,
Where Jesus reigns in glory,
  A home of peace and joy.
No home on earth is like it,
  Or can with it compare;
For every one is happy,
  Nor could be happier there.

Albert Midlane (1825–1909)

I Think Heaven Will Have...

I think at the gold gates,
Angels stand ready to greet us,
There is a long thin stream
Through the middle of Heaven,
In the stream lilies float along.

As we walk through, angels fly
Around laughing, smiling and
Having fun,
There are meadows of flowers.

We get to a big gold garden house,
In it is a big chair (gold of course),
On the chair sits God himself,
On the table there is a big book
With pages and pages of names.

He looks up at us with shining eyes,
He says 'The angel Gabriel will take you
To meet the rest of the angels here,
I hope it is all you ever dreamed of.'

I have seen everything now
But there is something that I would like
  more than everything,
I need my family and friends with me.

I cannot give you them I am afraid,
But as you are now an angel,
You can go back to Earth anytime
To see them, but remember they cannot
  see you,
Or hear you,
But you can send messages to their minds.

Emma Kew (aged 10)
To Nan

The Land That Breaks Beyond Our Dreams

The land that breaks
beyond our dreams
has crocuses that do not dip
below the earth of winter;
and it is only their mood there
which makes the petals cup in prayer
or spread with joy.

The land that breaks
beyond our dreams
only breathes the virgin air
of itself, and the roaming rainbows
of its ribbon afternoons;
when the birdsong scoops the
too-long dead from our
mean, untidy graves.

The land that breaks
beyond our dreams
is where the drained begin to leap
and the faint rustle of the
butterfly's waltz
is enough to kneel you deep,
tame with yourself
and sluiced of all your woes.

The land that breaks
beyond our dreams
where all that glory comes beside us,
and surging shoals of daffodils
surf across an ocean, or,
perhaps a cloud;
that will be when
there is no more proud;
and the missing, the mad,
and the cowed,
will know how to sing descant
with the voice behind the nightingale.

Stewart Henderson (Modern poet)

The Guardian Angel

Thou angel of God who hast charge of me
From the dear Father of mercifulness,
The shepherding kind of the fold of the saints
To make round about me this night.

Drive from me every temptation and danger,
Surround me on the sea of unrighteousness,
And in the narrows, crooks, and straits,
Keep thou my coracle, keep it always.

Be thou a bright flame before me,
Be thou a guiding star above me,
Be thou a smooth path below me,
And be a kindly shepherd behind me,
Today, tonight, and for ever.

I am tired and I a stranger,
Lead thou me to the land of angels;
For me it is time to go home
To the court of Christ, to the peace of heaven.

From *Carmina Gadelica*

Prayer at Bedtime

Matthew, Mark, Luke and John
Bless the bed that I lie on.
Before I lay me down to sleep,
I pray the Lord my soul to keep.

Four corners to my bed,
Four angels there are spread;
Two at the foot, two at the head:
Four to carry me when I'm dead.

I go by sea, I go by land:
The Lord made me with His right hand.
Should any danger come to me,
Sweet Jesus Christ deliver me.

He's the branch and I'm the flower,
Pray God send me a happy hour;
And should I die before I wake,
I pray the Lord my soul to take.

Anonymous

First Lines